BOOK FOUR
words edition

THANKYOU MUSIC
NASHVILLE U.S.A.

KINGSWAY MUSIC
EASTBOURNE U.K

All enquiries regarding the reproduction of
Thankyou Music songs in North America should be directed to
Maranatha! Music, PO Box 31050,
Laguna Hills, CA 92654 1050.

North American distributors:
Thankyou Music Inc., c/o Alexandria House Inc.
468 McNally Drive, Nashville, TN 37211.

Printed in Great Britain for
KINGSWAY MUSIC LTD
1 St Anne's Road, Eastbourne, E Sussex BN21 3UN by
Richard Clay Ltd, Bungay, Suffolk.
Typeset by Nuprint Ltd, Harpenden, Herts.

1

ALL HAIL THE LAMB, enthroned on high;
His praise shall be our battle cry.
He reigns victorious, forever glorious,
His name is Jesus, He is the Lord.

2

ALL HEAVEN DECLARES
The glory of the risen Lord.
Who can compare
With the beauty of the Lord?
Forever He will be
The Lamb upon the throne.
I gladly bow the knee
And worship Him alone.

I will proclaim
The glory of the risen Lord,
Who once was slain
To reconcile man to God.
Forever You will be
The Lamb upon the throne.
I gladly bow the knee
And worship You alone.

3

ALL HEAVEN WAITS with bated breath,
For saints on earth to pray.
Majestic angels ready stand
With swords of fiery blade.
Astounding power awaits a word
From God's resplendent throne.
But God awaits our prayer of faith
That cries 'Your will be done.'

Awake, O church, arise and pray;
Complaining words discard.
The Spirit comes to fill your mouth
With truth, His mighty sword.
Go place your feet on Satan's ground
And there proclaim Christ's name,
In step with heaven's armies march
To conquer and to reign!

Now in our hearts and on our lips
The word of faith is near,
Let heaven's will on earth be done,
Let heaven flow from here.
Come blend your prayers with Jesus' own
Before the Father's throne,
And as the incense clouds ascend
God's holy fire rains down.

Soon comes the day when with a shout
King Jesus shall appear,
And with Him all the church,
From every age, shall fill the air.
The brightness of His coming shall
Consume the lawless one,
As with a word the breath of God
Tears down his rebel throne.

One body here, by heaven inspired,
We seek prophetic power;
In Christ agreed, one heart and voice,
To speak this day, this hour,
In every place where chaos rules
And evil forces brood;
Let Jesus' voice speak like the roar
Of a great multitude.

4

ALMIGHTY GOD, OUR HEAVENLY FATHER,
We have sinned against You,
And against our fellow men,
In thought and word and deed,
Through negligence, through weakness,
Through our own deliberate fault.
We are truly sorry
And repent of all our sins.
For the sake of Your Son Jesus Christ,
Who died for us,
Who died for us,
Who died for us,
Forgive us all that is past;
And grant that we may serve You
In newness of life.
To the glory of Your name, *(Men)*
To the glory of Your name, *(Women)*
To the glory of Your name, *(Men)*
To the glory of Your name, *(Women)*
To the glory of Your name. *(All)*
Amen, amen.

5

**ALMIGHTY GOD, WE THANK YOU FOR
   FEEDING US,**
With the body and blood of Your Son,
   Jesus Christ.
Through Him we offer You our souls and
   bodies,
To be a living sacrifice;
Send us out in the power of Your Spirit,
To live and work to Your praise and glory.

6
Phil Lawson Johnston.
Copyright © Thankyou Music 1987.

ALMIGHTY SOVEREIGN LORD, Creator God,
You made the heavens and the earth.
You've spoken to the world,
Yourself the living Word,
You give us eyes to see Your kingdom.

So stretch out Your hand, O God,
In signs and wonders,
We rest our faith on Your almighty power.
Stretch out Your hand, O God,
To heal and deliver. We declare,
We declare Your kingdom is here.

Stir up Your people like a mighty wind,
Come shake us, wake us from our sleep.
Give us compassion, Lord,
Love for Your holy word,
Give us the courage of Your kingdom.

Why do so many stand against You now,
Bringing dishonour to Your name?
Consider how they mock,
But we will never stop
Speaking with boldness of Your kingdom.

7
Cathy Carter/Bob Fitts.
Copyright © Thankyou Music 1989.

AS WE WORSHIP in Your presence,
There is healing;
The Holy Spirit's gentle touch
Is flowing:
Jesus, we believe,
Jesus, there's healing in Your name.
(Repeat)

Almighty Father,
We lift our hands to You,
We receive Your power
To heal as You would do.

8
Graham Kendrick.
Copyright © Make Way Music/
Thankyou Music 1988.

AT THIS TIME OF GIVING,
Gladly now we bring
Gifts of goodness and mercy
From a heavenly King.

Earth could not contain the treasures
Heaven holds for you,
Perfect joy and lasting pleasures,
Love so strong and true.

May His tender love surround you
At this Christmastime;
May you see His smiling face
That in the darkness shines.

But the many gifts He gives
Are all poured out from one;
Come receive the greatest gift,
The gift of God's own Son.

Lai, lai, lai…(etc.)

9
Morris Chapman.
Copyright © Word Music (UK) 1983.

BE BOLD, BE STRONG,
For the Lord your God is with you.
Be bold, be strong,
For the Lord your God is with you.
I am not afraid,
I am not dismayed,
Because I'm walking in faith and victory,
Come on and walk in faith and victory,
For the Lord your God is with you.

10
Dave Evans.
Copyright © Thankyou Music 1986.

BE STILL, for the presence of the Lord,
the Holy One is here;
Come bow before Him now with reverence
and fear.
In Him no sin is found, we stand
on holy ground;
Be still, for the presence of the Lord,
the Holy One is here.

Be still, for the glory of the Lord
is shining all around;
He burns with holy fire, with splendour
He is crowned.
How awesome is the sight, our radiant
King of light;
Be still, for the glory of the Lord
is shining all around.

Be still, for the power of the Lord
is moving in this place;
He comes to cleanse and heal, to minister
His grace.
No work too hard for Him, in faith
receive from Him;
Be still, for the power of the Lord
is moving in this place.

11

CHRIST IS RISEN!
Hallelujah, hallelujah!
Christ is risen!
Risen indeed, hallelujah!

Love's work is done,
The battle is won.
Where now, O death, is your sting?
He rose again
To rule and to reign,
Jesus our conquering King.

Lord over sin,
Lord over death,
At His feet Satan must fall!
Every knee bow,
All will confess
Jesus is Lord over all!

Tell it abroad
'Jesus is Lord!'
Shout it and let your praise ring!
Gladly we raise
Our songs of praise,
Worship is our offering.

12

CLEANSE ME, O GOD;
Cleanse me with Your blood.
Remember not my sin;
Cleanse me from within.

Cleanse me, O God,
And yet Your river flow.
Purify my heart;
Let Your grace and mercy flow.

13

CLEAR THE ROAD, make wide the way.　*(echo)*
Welcome now the God who saves.　*(echo)*
Fill the streets with shouts of joy.　*(echo)*
(Cheers, etc.)

    Prepare the way of the Lord!　*(echo)*
    Prepare the way of the Lord!　*(echo)*

Raise your voice and join the song,　*(echo)*
God made flesh to us has come.　*(echo)*
Welcome Him, your banners wave.　*(echo)*
(Cheers, shouts, wave banners, etc.)

For all sin the price is paid,　*(echo)*
All our sins on Jesus laid.　*(echo)*
By His blood we are made clean.　*(echo)*
(Cheers, shouts of thanksgiving)

At His feet come humbly bow,　*(echo)*
In your lives enthrone Him now.　*(echo)*
See, your great Deliverer comes.　*(echo)*
(Cheers, shouts welcoming Jesus)

14

(Men)　　　　　　　　*(Women)*
COME, HOLY SPIRIT,　hear us calling,
Come, Holy Spirit,　　hear us calling,
Come, Holy Spirit,　　hear us calling to You,
Come, Holy Spirit,　　hear us calling,
(All)
Hear us calling
Hear us calling to You.

(Men)　　　　　　　　*(Women)*
Come give Your gifts,　edify Your church,
Come bring Your truth,　glorify our Lord,
Come be our guide,　　point the way
(All)
Come walk beside.

15

COME INTO THE HOLY OF HOLIES,
Enter by the blood of the Lamb;
Come into His presence with singing,
Worship at the throne of God.
(Repeat)

Lifting holy hands
To the King of kings,
Worship Jesus.

16

COME, LET US SING for joy to the Lord,
Come let us sing for joy to the Lord,
Come let us sing for joy to the Lord,
Come let us sing for joy to the Lord!

    Come let us sing for joy to the Lord,
    Let us shout aloud to the Rock of our
      salvation!
(Repeat)

Let us come before Him with thanksgiving,
And extol Him with music and song;
For the Lord, our Lord, is a great God,
The great King above all gods.

Let us bow before Him in our worship,
Let us kneel before God, our great King;
For He is our God, and we are His people,
That's why we shout and sing!

17 Graham Kendrick.
Copyright © Make Way Music/
Thankyou Music 1985.

DARKNESS LIKE A SHROUD covers the earth;
Evil like a cloud covers the people.
But the Lord will rise upon you,
And His glory will appear on you—
Nations will come to your light.

> *Arise, shine, your light has come,*
> *The glory of the Lord has risen on you!*
> *Arise, shine, your light has come,*
> *Jesus the Light of the world has come.*

Children of the light, be clean and pure
Rise, you sleepers, Christ will shine on you.
Take the Spirit's flashing two-edged sword
And with faith declare God's mighty word;
Stand up and in His strength be strong.

Here among us now, Christ the light
Kindles brighter flames in our trembling hearts!
Living Word, our Lamp, come guide our feet
As we walk as one in light and peace,
'Til justice and truth shine like the sun.

Like a city bright so let us blaze;
Lights in every street turning night to day.
And the darkness shall not overcome
Till the fullness of Christ's kingdom comes,
Dawning to God's eternal day.

18 Stuart De Vane & Glenn Gore.
Copyright © Mercy Publishing/
Thankyou Music 1987.

DRAW ME CLOSER, Lord,
Draw me closer, dear Lord,
So that I might touch You,
So that I might touch You,
Lord I want to touch You.

Touch my eyes, Lord,
Touch my eyes, dear Lord,
So that I might see You,
So that I might see You,
Lord I want to see You.

Your glory, Your love,
Your glory, Your love,
Your glory, Your love,
And Your majesty.

19 Michael Card.
Copyright © Whole Armor Publishing (USA) 1982.

EL-SHADDAI, El-Shaddai,
El-Elyon na Adonai,
Age to age You're still the same
By the power of the name.
El-Shaddai, El-Shaddai,
Erkamka na Adonai,
We will praise and lift You high.
El-Shaddai.

Through Your love and through the ram
You saved the son of Abraham;
Through the power of Your hand,
Turned the sea into dry land.
To the outcast on her knees
You were the God who really sees,
And by Your might You set Your children free.

Through the years You made it clear
That the time of Christ was near;
Though the people couldn't see
What Messiah ought to be.
Though Your word contained the plan,
They just could not understand
Your most awesome work was done
Through the frailty of Your Son.

20 John Watson.
Copyright © Ampelos Music/
Thankyou Music 1987.

FATHER, I NEED YOU, searched for Your love;
Years spent without You, no one to love.
Now You're very near me, Your child I've
become;
Father, You're becoming so real to me.
So real to me, so real to me,
Father, You're becoming so real to me.

Now I stand, drawn by Your hand
From a life of heartache, fear and despair.
Your body it was broken, Your blood shed for
me;
Jesus, You're becoming so real to me.
So real to me, so real to me,
Jesus, You're becoming so real to me.

Then I bowed before Your throne,
Weary and tired, no power in my life.
Then, Holy Spirit, You came down on me;
Spirit, You're becoming so real to me.
So real to me, so real to me,
Spirit You're becoming so real to me.

(Last time)
So real to me, so real to me,
Father, You're becoming,
Jesus, You're becoming,
Spirit, You're becoming
So real to me.

21

FATHER IN HEAVEN,
Our voices we raise,
Receive our devotion,
Receive now our praise;
As we sing of the glory
Of all that You've done,
The greatest love story
That's ever been sung.

And we will crown You Lord of all,
Yes, we will crown You Lord of all,
For You have won the victory,
Yes we will crown You Lord of all.

Father in heaven,
Our lives are Your own;
We've been caught by a vision
Of Jesus alone,
Who came as a servant
To free us from sin,
Father in heaven,
Our worship we bring:

We will sing 'Hallelujah',
We will sing to the King,
To our Mighty Deliverer
Our hallelujahs will ring.
Yes, our praise is resounding
To the Lamb on the throne,
He alone is exalted
Through the love He has shown.

22

FATHER IN HEAVEN HOW WE LOVE YOU,
We lift Your name in all the earth,
May Your kingdom be established in our praises
As Your people declare Your mighty works.
Blessèd be the Lord God Almighty,
Who was and is and is to come;
Blessèd be the Lord God Almighty,
Who reigns for evermore.

23

FATHER, YOU ARE MY PORTION in this life,
And You are my hope and my delight,
And I love You, yes I love You,
Lord I love You, my delight.

Jesus, You are my treasure in this life,
And You are so pure and so kind,
And I love You, yes I love You,
Lord I love You, my delight.

24

FATHER, YOU'RE ENTHRONED on the praises
    of Your people,
Your name is high over all;
Commanding creation as You reign in awesome
    splendour,
We bow before Your throne.

As we worship You, come to us, Father,
Fill us Lord and make us new;
As we worship You, make us holy,
Help us, Lord, to be more like You.

Jesus, You shine on the faces of Your children,
Your name is high over all.
You humbled Yourself so that we might be
    forgiven,
We bow before You now.

Spirit, You come and You help us in our
    weakness,
Your name is high over all.
You give us the power to follow after Jesus,
We humbly ask You now.

25 Bonnie Low.
Copyright © Scripture in Song 1977, 1982.

FOR THE LORD IS MARCHING ON,
And His army is ever strong;
And His glory shall be seen upon our land.
Raise the anthem, sing the victor's song.
Praise the Lord for the battle's won.
No weapon formed against us shall stand.

For the Captain of the host is Jesus.
We're following in His footsteps,
No foe can stand against us in the fray.
(Repeat)

We are marching in Messiah's band,
The keys of victory in His mighty hand.
Let us march on to take our promised land.
For the Lord is marching on,
And His army is ever strong;
And His glory shall be seen upon our land.

26 Graham Kendrick.
Copyright © Make Way Music/
Thankyou Music 1987.

FROM THE SUN'S RISING
Unto the sun's setting,
Jesus our Lord
Shall be great in the earth;
And all earth's kingdoms
Shall be His dominion,
All of creation
Shall sing of His worth.

Let every heart, every voice,
Every tongue join with spirits ablaze;
One in His love, we will circle the world
With the song of His praise.
Oh, let all His people rejoice,
And let all the earth hear His voice!

To every tongue, tribe
And nation He sends us,
To make disciples
To teach and baptise.
For all authority
To Him is given;
Now as His witnesses
We shall arise.

Come let us join with
The church from all nations,
Cross every border,
Throw wide every door;
Workers with Him
As He gathers His harvest,
Till earth's far corners
Our Saviour adore.

27 Henry Smith.
Copyright © Integrity's Hosanna! Music 1978

GIVE THANKS with a grateful heart.
Give thanks to the Holy One.
Give thanks because He's given
Jesus Christ, His Son.
(Repeat)

And now let the weak say 'I am strong',
Let the poor say 'I am rich',
Because of what the Lord has done for us.
(Repeat)

(Last time)
Give thanks.

28 Danny Reed.
Copyright © Thankyou Music 1987.

GLORIOUS FATHER, we exalt You,
We worship, honour and adore You.
We delight to be in Your presence, O Lord,
We magnify Your holy name.

And we sing come, Lord Jesus,
Glorify Your name.
And we sing come, Lord Jesus,
Glorify Your name.

29 Danny Daniels.
Copyright © Mercy Publishing/
Thankyou Music 1987.

GLORY, glory in the highest;
Glory, to the Almighty;
Glory to the Lamb of God,
And glory to the living Word;
Glory to the Lamb!

I give glory, (glory)
Glory, (glory)
Glory, glory to the Lamb!
I give glory, (glory)
Glory, (glory)
Glory, glory to the Lamb!
I give glory to the Lamb!

30 Steve McEwan.
Copyright © Dawn Treader Music/
Friends First Music/Word Music (UK) 1985.

GREAT IS THE LORD and most worthy of praise,
The city of our God, the holy place,
The joy of the whole earth.
Great is the Lord in whom we have the victory,
He aids us against the enemy,
We bow down on our knees.

And Lord, we want to lift Your name on high,
And Lord, we want to thank You,
For the works You've done in our lives;
And Lord, we trust in Your unfailing love,
For You alone are God eternal,
Throughout earth and heaven above.

31 Wynne Goss.
Copyright © Morningsong Music/
Thankyou Music 1988.

HALLELUJAH, HE IS HERE.
Hallelujah, He is here.
And my heart overflows
With the love that He shows.
Hallelujah, He is here.

32 David Fellingham.
Copyright © Thankyou Music 1988.

HEAR, O SHEPHERD of Your people,
Let Your face shine and we will be saved.
Shine forth, O God, in this pagan darkness.
Awaken Your power, and come to restore.

O Lord of hosts, turn again now,
Make Your church strong to speak out Your
word.
We'll not turn back from our great
commission
To reach the lost and save this land.

Let Your power fall upon us,
Give strength unto the sons of Your right hand.
We now hear the call to seek You,
Awaken Your power, and come to restore.

33 Graham Kendrick.
Copyright © Make Way Music/
Thankyou Music 1987.

HE HAS SHOWED YOU, O MAN, what is good,
And what does the Lord require of you.
He has showed you, O man, what is good,
And what does the Lord require of you;
But to act justly, and to love mercy,
And to walk humbly with your God;
But to act justly, and to love mercy,
And to walk humbly with your God.

34 Twila Paris.
Copyright © Straightway Music/
Word Music (UK) 1985.

HE IS EXALTED,
The King is exalted on high,
I will praise Him.
He is exalted,
Forever exalted
And I will praise His name!

He is the Lord,
Forever His truth shall reign.
Heaven and earth
Rejoice in His holy name.
He is exalted,
The King is exalted on high!

35 Robert Lowry.

HERE IS LOVE vast as the ocean,
Loving kindness as the flood,
When the Prince of life, our ransom
Shed for us His precious blood.
Who His love will not remember?
Who can cease to sing His praise?
He can never be forgotten
Throughout heaven's eternal days.

On the Mount of Crucifixion
Fountains opened deep and wide;
Through the floodgates of God's mercy
Flowed a vast and gracious tide.
Grace and love, like mighty rivers,
Poured incessant from above,
And heaven's peace and perfect justice
Kissed a guilty world in love.

36 Steve Hampton.
Copyright © Scripture in Song/
Thankyou Music 1978.

HERE WE ARE,
Gathered together as a family;
Bound as one,
Lifting up our voices
To the King of kings.
We cry:

Abba, Father, worthy is Your name.
Abba, Father, worthy is Your name.

Here, we are,
Singing together as a family;
Bound as one,
Lifting up our voices
To the King of kings.
We sing:

Abba, Father, holy is Your name.
Abba, Father, holy is Your name.

37

HE THAT IS IN US is greater than He
That is in the world.
He that is in us is greater than he
That is in the world.

Therefore I will sing and I will rejoice
For His Spirit lives in me.
Christ the Living One has overcome
And we share in His victory.

All the powers of death and hell and sin
Lie crushed beneath His feet;
Jesus owns the Name above all names
Crowned with honour and majesty.

38

HE WALKED WHERE I WALK,   *(echo)*
He stood where I stand,   *(echo)*
He felt what I feel,   *(echo)*
He understands.   *(echo)*
He knows my frailty,   *(echo)*
Shared my humanity,   *(echo)*
Tempted in every way,   *(echo)*
Yet without sin.   *(echo)*

   God with us, so close to us.
   God with us, Immanuel!

One of a hated race,   *(echo)*
Stung by the prejudice,   *(echo)*
Suffering injustice,   *(echo)*
Yet He forgives.   *(echo)*
Wept for my wasted years,   *(echo)*
Paid for my wickedness,   *(echo)*
He died in my place   *(echo)*
That I might live.   *(echo)*

39

HE WAS PIERCED for our transgressions,
And bruised for our iniquities;
And to bring us peace He was punished,
And by His stripes we are healed.

He was led like a lamb to the slaughter,
Although He was innocent of crime;
And cut off from the land of the living,
He paid for the guilt that was mine.

We like sheep have gone astray,
Turned each one to his own way,
And the Lord has laid on Him
The iniquity of us all.

(Descant)
Like a lamb,
To the slaughter He came.
And the Lord laid on Him
The iniquity of us all.

40

HOLY IS THE LORD OUR GOD.
Blessed is His holy name.
Perfect is His love to us,
Holy is His name.

41

HOLY SPIRIT, WE WELCOME YOUR PRESENCE.
Holy Spirit, we know that You are with us.
Let Your presence fill this place;
Let us see You face to face;
In the light of Your holiness we stand broken;
In the light of Your holiness we stand open
To do Your will with our whole lives.

(all) **42**

HOSANNA, hosanna, hosanna in the highest.
Hosanna, hosanna, hosanna in the highest.
Lord we lift up Your name, with hearts full of
   praise,
Be exalted, O Lord, my God,
Hosanna in the highest.

Glory, glory, glory to the King of kings.
Glory, glory, glory to the King of kings.
Lord, we lift up Your name, with hearts full of
   praise,
Be exalted, O Lord, my God,
Glory to the King of kings.

43

HOW YOU BLESS OUR LIVES, Lord God!
How You fill our lives, Lord God!
I simply want to say I love You, Lord.
I simply want to say I bless You,
I simply want to say I adore You,
And I want to lift Your name even higher.

44
Danny Daniels.
Copyright © Mercy Publishing/
Thankyou Music 1985.

I AM A WOUNDED SOLDIER but I will not leave
the fight,
Because the Great Physician is healing me.
So I'm standing in the battle, in the armour of
His light,
Because His mighty power is real in me.

I am loved, I am accepted,
By the Saviour of my soul.
I am loved, I am accepted
And my wounds will be made whole.

45
David J Hadden.
Copyright © Restoration Music Ltd 1983.

I AM PERSUADED that neither death nor life,
Nor angels, principalities, nor powers,
Nor things that are now, nor things that are to
come,
Can separate us from the love of God.

We are more than conquerors
We are more than conquerors,
We are more than conquerors,
In Christ, in Christ.

46
Don Moen.
Copyright © Integrity's Hosanna! Music 1985.

I AM THE GOD THAT HEALETH THEE,
I am the Lord, your healer.
I sent My word and healed your disease,
I am the Lord, your healer.

You are the God that healeth me,
You are the Lord, my healer.
You sent Your word and healed my disease,
You are the Lord, my healer.

47
Marc Nelson.
Copyright © Mercy Publishing/
Thankyou Music 1987.

I BELIEVE IN JESUS:
I believe He is the Son of God,
I believe He died and rose again,
I believe He paid for us all.

(Men)   And I believe He's here now,
(Women) I believe that He is here.
(All)   Standing in our midst.
(Men)   Here with the power to heal now,
(Women) With the power to heal,
All)   And the grace to forgive.

I believe in You, Lord;
I believe You are the Son of God,
I believe You died and rose again,
I believe You paid for us all.

(Men)   And I believe You're here now.
(Women) I believe that You're here.
(All)   Standing in our midst.
(Men)   Here with the power to heal now,
(Women) With the power to heal,
(All)   And the grace to forgive.

48
Hanneke Jacobs.
Copyright © Maranatha Music USA/
Word Music 1985.

I CAN ALMOST SEE Your holiness,
As I look around this place,
With my hands stretched out,
To receive Your love,
I can see You on each face.

Spirit of God, lift me up,
Spirit of God, lift me up,
Fill me again with Your love,
Sweet Spirit of God.
    (Repeat)

49
Phil Rogers.
Copyright © Thankyou Music 1988.

I CANNOT COUNT YOUR BLESSINGS LORD,
They're wonderful.
I can't begin to measure Your great love,
I cannot count the times You have forgiven me,
And changed me by Your Spirit from above.

How I worship You my Father, You are
    wonderful,
How I glorify You Jesus, You're my Lord.
How I praise You Holy Spirit,
You have changed my life,
And You're now at work in me to change the
    world.

When I was blind You opened up my eyes to
see,
When I was dead You gave me life anew;
When I was lost You found me and You rescued
me,
And carried me, rejoicing, home with You.

I cannot count Your mercies, Lord,
They're marvellous,
I can't begin to measure Your great grace;
I cannot count the times that You have
answered me,
Whenever I have prayed and sought Your face.

Whenever I consider what I am to You,
My heart is filled with wonder, love and awe;
I want to share with others that You love them
  too,
And tell the world of Jesus, more and more.

50

IF MY PEOPLE WHO BEAR MY NAME
Will humble themselves and pray;
If they seek my presence
And turn their backs on their wicked ways;
Then I will hear from heaven,
I'll hear from heaven and will forgive.
I will forgive their sins
And will heal their land—
Yes, I will heal their land.

51

I GIVE YOU NOW all I have;
I give to you my everything.
You have the power inside of you
To overcome all the hosts of darkness.

  Go, go into the world,
  Tell them I'm alive,
  Go into the streets,
  Tell them that I live,
  Ooh, that I live in you.
  Go, go into the world,
  Claim it for your King,
  Go into the streets,
  Dry those people's tears,
  Ooh, make the old things new.

52

  I HAVE A DESTINY *I know I shall fulfil,*
  I have a destiny in that city on a hill.
  I have a destiny and it's not an empty wish,
  For I know I was born for such a time as this.

Long before the ages You predestined me
To walk in all the works You have prepared for
  me.
You've given me a part to play in history
To help prepare a bride for eternity.

I did not choose You but You have chosen me
And appointed me for bearing fruit abundantly.
I know You will complete the work begun in me,
By the power of Your Spirit working mightily.

53

I JUST WANT TO PRAISE YOU, I just want to
  sing.
I just want to give You, Lord, my everything,
In every situation, in everything I do,
To give You my devotion, for my delight is You

  Lord, I lift You high.
  Your love will never die.

54

I LIFT MY HANDS   *(echo)*
To the coming King,   *(echo)*
To the great I AM,   *(echo)*
To You I sing,   *(echo)*
For You're the One   *(echo)*
Who reigns within my heart.   *(all)*

  And I will serve no foreign god,
  Or any other treasure.
  You are my heart's desire,
  Spirit without measure.
  Unto Your name
  I will bring my sacrifice.

55

I LIFT MY VOICE to praise Your name,
That through my life I might proclaim
The praises of the One who reigns:
Jesus, my Lord.

Like a mighty flame that burns so bright,
I am a bearer of His light.
No longer I, for He is my life:
Jesus, my Lord.

  Jesus, Jesus, alive in me.
  Jesus, Jesus, setting me free.

56

I'M ACCEPTED, I'm forgiven,
I am fathered by the true and living God.
I'm accepted, no condemnation,
I am loved by the true and living God.
There's no guilt or fear as I draw near
To the Saviour and Creator of the world.
There is joy and peace
As I release my worship to You, O Lord.

IMMANUEL, O IMMANUEL,
Bowed in awe I worship at Your feet,
And sing Immanuel, God is with us;
Sharing my humanness, my shame,
Feeling my weaknesses, my pain,
Taking the punishment, the blame,
Immanuel.
And now my words cannot explain,
All that my heart cannot contain,
How great are the glories of Your name,
Immanuel.

IN HEAVENLY ARMOUR we'll enter the land,
The battle belongs to the Lord.
No weapon that's fashioned against us will
  stand,
The battle belongs to the Lord.

  And we sing glory, honour,
  Power and strength to the Lord.
  We sing glory, honour,
  Power and strength to the Lord.

When the power of darkness comes in like a
  flood,
The battle belongs to the Lord.
He's raised up a standard, the power of His
  blood,
The battle belongs to the Lord.

When your enemy presses in hard, do not fear,
The battle belongs to the Lord.
Take courage, my friend, your redemption is
  near.
The battle belongs to the Lord.

IN MOMENTS LIKE THESE I sing out a song,
I sing out a love song to Jesus.
In moments like these I lift up my hands,
I lift up my hands to the Lord.

  Singing, I love You, Lord,
  Singing, I love You, Lord,
  Singing, I love You, Lord,
  I love You.

IN THE TOMB SO COLD they laid Him,
Death its victim claimed.
Powers of hell they could not hold Him;
Back to life He came!

  Christ is risen! (Christ is risen!)
  Death has been conquered. (Death has been
    conquered.)
  Christ is risen! (Christ is risen!)
  He shall reign for ever.

Hell had spent its fury on Him,
Left Him crucified.
Yet, by blood, He boldly conquered,
Sin and death defied.

Now the fear of death is broken,
Love has won the crown.
Prisoners of the darkness listen,
Walls are tumbling down.

Raised from death to heaven ascending
Love's exalted King.
Let His son of joy, unending,
Through the nations ring!

IT IS YOU, it is You,
It is You that I love.
It is You, my Lord and King,
I apprehend to know and be known.
You, it is You,
It is You that I worship.
Holy, holy,
Worthy, yes, You're worthy.
How I love You, Lord.

IT'S YOUR BLOOD that cleanses me,
It's Your blood that gives me life.
It's Your blood that took my place,
In redeeming sacrifice;
Washes me whiter than the snow, than the
  snow,
My Jesus, God's precious sacrifice.

63

I WANT TO BE A PART OF YOUR ARMY,
Lord, count me in, oh, count me in.
I want to have a destiny in You;
To shine a light across this land,
To be strong and take a stand;
In Your kingdom plan,
Lord, count me in.

Let my heart serve You,
Let my mind serve too;
Let my will be Your own.
I want to be a part of Your army,
Lord, count me in, oh, count me in,
In Your kingdom plan,
Lord, count me in.

64

I WANT TO SERVE THE PURPOSE OF GOD
In my generation.
I want to serve the purpose of God
While I am alive.
I want to give my life
For something that will last forever.
O I delight, I delight to do Your will.

I want to build with silver and gold
In my generation.
I want to build with silver and gold
While I am alive.
I want to give my life
For something that will last forever.
O I delight, I delight to do Your will.

What is on Your heart?
Tell me what to do;
Let me know Your will
And I will follow You.
    (Repeat)

I want to see the kingdom of God
In my generation.
I want to see the kingdom of God
While I am alive.
I want to live my life
For something that will last forever.
O I delight, I delight to do Your will.

I want to see the Lord come again
In my generation.
I want to see the Lord come again
While I am alive.
I want to give my life
For something that will last forever.
O I delight, I delight to do Your will.
O I delight, I delight to do Your will.

65

I WANT TO SING A PRAISE SONG TO YOU,
I want to lift the name of Jesus higher,
I want to sing, I want to move my feet,
Lord, I'm gonna worship You.

I want to praise, praise You, Lord,
I want to praise, praise You, Lord,
I want to praise You, Lord,
You're worthy to be praised,
Praise the Lord with me.

66

I WANT TO THANK YOU LORD for loving
    me.
Oh, I give my praise to You.
I want to thank You Lord for loving me,
Oh, I give my praise to You.

I will remember Your goodness, Lord,
I will remember Your kindness.
You turned my sorrow to shouts of joy.
You are the light of my life!

I will remember Your power, Lord,
I will remember Your mercy.
I will remember You rescued me.
Your love has captured my heart!

67

I WILL BUILD MY CHURCH,   *(Men)*
I will build My church,   *(Women)*
And the gates of hell   *(Men)*
And the gates of hell   *(Women)*
Shall not prevail   *(Men)*
Shall not prevail   *(Women)*
Against it.   *(All)*
(Repeat)

So you powers in the heavens above, bow
  down!
And you powers on the earth below, bow down!
And acknowledge that Jesus,
Jesus, Jesus, is Lord, is Lord.

68 D J Butler.
Copyright © Mercy Publishing/
Thankyou Music 1987.

I WILL CHANGE YOUR NAME,
You shall no longer be called
Wounded, outcast, lonely or afraid.
I will change your name,
Your new name shall be,
Confidence, joyfulness, overcoming one;
Faithfulness, friend of God,
One who seeks My face.

69 Dave Bilbrough.
Copyright © Dave Bilbrough Songs/
Thankyou Music 1986.

I WILL EXALT YOUR NAME, LORD JESUS,
Your faithful love I will declare.
My heart is fixed on You Lord Jesus,
I'll sing of Your praises everywhere.

Blessings each day, flowing from Jesus,
Mercy and grace beyond compare;
My all sufficiency throughout eternity,
Your faithful love I will declare.

70 Lynn DeShazo.
Copyright © Lynn DeShazo/Thankyou Music 1986.

I WILL JOY OVER YOU with thanksgiving;
I will sing Your praise.
I will laugh with delight at Your goodness;
I will sing, I will sing the glory of Your name!

The Lord most high is a mighty rock!   *(Men)*
The Lord is high and exalted!   *(Women)*
The Lord of hosts is a mighty God!   *(Men)*
The Lord of life is my delight!   *(All)*

71 Scott Palazzo.
Copyright © Mercy Publishing/
Thankyou Music 1985.

I WILL MAGNIFY Thy name
Above all the earth.
I will magnify Thy name
Above all the earth.

I will sing unto Thee
The praises of my heart.
I will sing unto Thee
The praises of my heart.

72 Phil Butson.
Copyright © Thankyou Music 1988.

I WILL PRAISE THE LORD with all of my heart,
May He be exalted.
I will praise the Lord with all of my heart,
May He be exalted;
Exalted.

I will lift my hands, adoring,
And with thankful heart I say:
In my life be exalted.

I will worship the Lord with all of my heart,
May He be exalted.
I will worship the Lord with all of my heart,
May He be exalted;
Exalted.

73 Daniel Gardner.
Copyright © Integrity's Hosanna! Music 1981.

I WILL WORSHIP YOU, LORD, with all of my
  might,
I will praise You with a psalm;
I will worship You, Lord, with all of my might,
I will praise You all day long.

For Thou, O Lord, art glorious,
And Thy name is greatly to be praised;
May my heart be pure and holy in Thy sight,
As I worship You with all of my might.

74 Sondra Corbett.
Copyright © Integrity's Hosanna! Music 1986.

I WORSHIP YOU, ALMIGHTY GOD,
There is none like You.
I worship You, O Prince of Peace,
That is what I love to do.
I give You praise,
For You are my righteousness.
I worship You, Almighty God,
There is none like You.

75

I WORSHIP YOU, *(Men)*
I worship You, *(Women)*
O Lamb of God *(All)*
Who takes away *(Men)*
Who takes away *(Women)*
The sin of the world. *(All)*
(Repeat)

    Alleluia, Alleluia,
    Alleluia, Alleluia.

I kneel before *(Men)*
I kneel before *(Women)*
The Lamb of God, *(All)*
Who takes away *(Men)*
Who takes away *(Women)*
The sin of the world. *(All)*

76

JEHOVAH JIREH, God will provide,
Jehovah Rophe, God heals;
Jehovah M'keddesh, God who sanctifies,
Jehovah Nissi, God is my banner.

Jehovah Rohi, God my shepherd,
Jehovah Shalom, God is peace;
Jehovah Tsidkenu, God our righteousness,
Jehovah Shammah, God who is there.

77

JEHOVAH JIREH, MY PROVIDER,
His grace is sufficient for me, for me, for me.
Jehovah Jireh, my Provider,
His grace is sufficient for me.

My God shall supply all my needs
According to His riches in glory;
He will give His angels charge over me,
Jehovah Jireh cares for me, for me, for me,
Jehovah Jireh cares for me.

78

JEHOVAH SHALOM,
The Lord is my strength and shield;
Jehovah Shalom,
To You I come and lay my burden down.

On You, for You are mighty,
On You, for You are able,
On You, our deliverer,
On You I put my trust.

Jehovah Shalom,
The Lord is my peace and joy;
Jehovah Shalom,
To You I come and lay my burden down.

(Last time)
Jehovah Shalom, Jehovah Shalom.

79

JESUS, I LOVE YOU;
I bow down before You.
Praises and worship
To our King.

Alleluia, alleluia;
Alleluia, allelu.

80

JESUS, KING OF KINGS,
We worship and adore You.
Jesus, Lord of heaven and earth,
We bow down at Your feet.
Father, we bring to You our worship;
Your sovereign will be done.
On earth Your kingdom come
Through Jesus Christ, Your only Son.

Jesus, Sovereign Lord,
We worship and adore You.
Jesus, Name above all names,
We bow down at Your feet.
Father, we offer You our worship;
Your sovereign will be done.
On earth Your kingdom come
Through Jesus Christ, Your only Son.

Jesus, Light of the world,
We worship and adore You.
Jesus, Lord Immanuel,
We bow down at Your feet.
Father, for Your delight we worship;
Your sovereign will be done,
On earth Your kingdom come
Through Jesus Christ, Your only Son.

81 Graham Kendrick.
Copyright © Thankyou Music 1986.

JESUS PUT THIS SONG INTO OUR HEARTS,
Jesus put this song into our hearts,
It's a song of joy no one can take away,
Jesus put this song into our hearts.

Jesus taught us how to live in harmony,
Jesus taught us how to live in harmony,
Different faces, different races, He made us one,
Jesus taught us how to live in harmony.

Jesus taught us how to be a family,
Jesus taught us how to be a family,
Loving one another with the love that He gives,
Jesus taught us how to be a family.

Jesus turned our sorrow into dancing,
Jesus turned our sorrow into dancing,
Changed our tears of sadness into rivers of joy,
Jesus turned our sorrow into a dance.

82 Chris Rolinson.
Copyright © Thankyou Music 1988.

JESUS, SEND MORE LABOURERS,
For, Lord, we see the need;
The land is ready for harvest,
The fields are ripe indeed.

Oh Lord but start with me,
Jesus begin with me,
Who will go for You, Lord?
Who will go for You, Lord?
Here I am, Lord,
Send me,
Send me, Lord,
Send me.

Lord, we love our country,
Countless lives to be won;
Jesus, bring revival,
That through us Your will be done.

Lord, we sense Your moving,
Touching our lives with power;
We are ready to serve You,
To go this day, this hour.

83 Chris A. Bowater.
Copyright © Lifestyle Ministries/
Word Music (UK) 1988.

JESUS SHALL TAKE THE HIGHEST HONOUR,
Jesus shall take the highest praise.
Let all earth join heaven in exalting
The Name which is above all other names.
Let's bow the knee in humble adoration,
For at His name every knee must bow;
Let every tongue confess He is Christ, God's
only Son.
Sovereign Lord we give you glory now,

For all honour and blessing and power,
Belongs to You, belongs to You;
All honour and blessing and power,
Belongs to You, belongs to You,
Lord Jesus Christ, Son of the living God.

84 Hilary Davies.
Copyright © Samsongs/Thankyou Music 1988.

JESUS, THE NAME ABOVE ALL NAMES,
Forever more the same,
And lifting up our hands we exalt You;
Come among us once again,
And glorify Your name,
So everyone will know
You are Emmanuel.

Emmanuel, Emmanuel,
Emmanuel, God is with us.

85 John Gibson.
Copyright © Thankyou Music 1987.

JESUS, WE CELEBRATE YOUR VICTORY:
Jesus, we revel in Your love.
Jesus, we rejoice, You've set us free;
Jesus, Your death has brought us life.

It was for freedom that Christ has set us free,
No longer to be subject to a yoke of slavery;
So we're rejoicing in God's victory,
Our hearts responding to His love.

His Spirit in us releases us from fear,
The way to Him is open, with boldness we draw
near;
And in His presence our problems disappear,
Our hearts responding to His love.

86 Dave Fellingham.
Copyright © Thankyou Music 1987.

JESUS YOU ARE THE POWER, You are the
wisdom
That comes from the Lord God, who has
revealed His love.
Our faith now rests on Your power,
Lord, which Your Spirit has poured out on us.

We declare the mystery hid before the ages,
Which God had planned for our glory.
For we have received a glorious inheritance
Pledged by the Spirit,
And our eyes have not seen, and our ears have
not heard
What is in store for the hearts of the ones
Who love the Lord.

87 Dave Fellingham.
Copyright © Thankyou Music 1987.

JESUS, YOU HAVE LIFTED ME,
Given me Your life;
You have heard my cry to You,
You have raised me up.
My heart trusts in You and I am helped;
You're my strength and shield.
My heart will rejoice,
And with my song I thank you, Lord.
You're my fortress and my rock—
I shall not be moved;
My life's hidden now with Christ in God—
I am now secure.

88 Isaac Watts.
Public Domain.

JOY TO THE WORLD! The Lord has come;
Let earth receive her King.
Let every heart prepare Him room,
And heaven and nature sing,
And heaven and nature sing,
And heaven, and heaven and nature sing!

Joy to the earth! The Saviour reigns;
Your sweetest songs employ.
While fields and streams and hills and plains
Repeat the sounding joy,
Repeat the sounding joy,
Repeat, repeat the sounding joy!

He rules the world with truth and grace,
And makes the nations prove
The glories of His righteousness,
The wonders of His love,
The wonders of His love,
The wonders, wonders of His love!

89 Patty Kennedy.
Copyright © Mercy Publishing/
Thankyou Music 1982.

JUST LIKE YOU PROMISED, You've come,
Just like You told us, You're here,
And our desire is that You know
We love You, we worship You,
We welcome You here.

90 Chris Cable.
Copyright © Coronation/
Thankyou Music 1988.

KEEPING MY EYES UPON YOU Lord,
Keeping my mind just stayed on You,
Giving to You my every fear, knowing You care;
Reign in my life, O Lord, I pray,
I want to live for You each day,
Casting my burden on You Lord,
Knowing You care.

91 Jane Norton.
Copyright © Thankyou Music 1986.

KING FOREVER, Lord Messiah,
He who was, and is, and is to come;
Prince of glory, name of Jesus,
Be Your praise and worship ever sung.

And we will sing hosanna to Jesus,
We exalt and raise Your name above;
And we proclaim the glory of Jesus,
Prince of peace, and worthy King of love.

Lord anointed, our salvation,
He whom angels call the Word of God;
True and faithful, Lamb of mercy,
Now receive our worship and our love.

92 Graham Kendrick.
Copyright © Make Way Music/
Thankyou Music 1988.

KING OF KINGS, Lord of lords,
Lion of Judah, Word of God.
King of kings, Lord of lords,
Lion of Judah, Word of God.

And here He comes, the King of glory comes!
In righteousness he comes to judge the earth.
And here He comes, the King of glory comes!
With justice He'll rule the earth.

93

LAMB OF GOD, Holy One,
Jesus Christ, Son of God,
Lifted up willingly to die,
That I the guilty one may know
The blood once shed, still freely flowing,
Still cleansing, still healing.

I exalt You, Jesus my sacrifice;
I exalt You, my Redeemer and my Lord.
I exalt You, worthy Lamb of God,
And in honour I bow down before Your
throne.

94

LET IT BE TO ME according to Your word.
Let it be to me according to Your word.
I am Your servant, no rights shall I demand.
Let it be to me, let it be to me,
Let it be to me according to Your word.

95

LET PRAISES RING, let praises ring,
Lift voices up to love Him,
Lift hearts and hands to touch Him,
O let praises ring.
And fill the skies with anthems high
That tell His excellencies,
As priests and kings who rule with Him
Through all eternity;

Let praises ring, let praises ring,
To our glorious King.

Let praises ring, let praises ring,
Bow down in adoration,
Cry out His exaltation,
O let praises ring.
And lift the name above all names
Till every nation knows
The love of God has come to men,
His mercies overflow.

96

LET US GO TO THE HOUSE OF THE LORD.
Let us go to the house of the Lord.
Let us go to the house of the Lord.

I rejoiced with those who said to me
'Let us go to the house of the Lord'.
Our feet are standing in your gates, Jerusalem;
Like a city built together,
Where the people of God go up
To praise the name of the Lord.

For peace for our Jerusalem
And loved ones this we pray;
May all men be secure where they must live.
And to all my friends and brothers,
May the peace be within you
For the sake of the house of the Lord.

97

LET US PRAISE HIS NAME WITH DANCING
And with the tambourine.
Let us praise His name with dancing,
Make a joyful noise and sing.

Dance, dance, dance before the King.
Dance, dance, celebrate and sing.

Let us celebrate with dancing;
The King has set us free.
Let us celebrate with dancing,
Rejoice in victory.

98

LET YOUR LIVING WATER FLOW over my soul.
Let Your Holy Spirit come and take control
Of every situation that has troubled my mind.
All my cares and burdens onto You I roll.

Jesus, Jesus, Jesus.
Father, Father, Father.
Spirit, Spirit, Spirit.

Come now, Holy Spirit, and take control.
Hold me in Your loving arms and make me
whole.
Wipe away all doubt and fear and take my pride,
Draw me to Your love and keep me by Your
side.

Give your life to Jesus, let Him fill Your soul.
Let Him take You in His arms and make you
whole.
As you give your life to Him He'll set You free.
You will live and reign with Him eternally.

99 Chris Rolinson.

LIGHTEN OUR DARKNESS, Lord we
  pray; *(echo)*
And in Your mercy defend us *(echo)*
From all perils and dangers of this
  night, *(echo)*
For the love of Your only Son, *(all)*
Our Saviour Jesus Christ.
Amen, Amen.
Amen, Amen.

100 Graham Kendrick.

LIGHT HAS DAWNED that ever shall blaze,
Darkness flees away.
Christ the light has shone in our hearts,
Turning night to day.

  We proclaim Him King of kings,
  We lift high His name.
  Heaven and earth shall bow at His feet
  When He comes to reign.

Saviour of the world is He,
Heaven's King come down.
Judgement, love and mercy meet
At His thorny crown.

Life has sprung from hearts of stone,
By the Spirit's breath.
Hell shall let her captives go,
Life has conquered death.

Blood has flowed that cleanses from sin,
God His love has proved.
Men may mock and demons may rage,
We shall not be moved!

101 Chris Rolinson.

LORD, COME AND HEAL YOUR CHURCH,
Take our lives and cleanse with Your fire.
Let Your deliverance flow,
As we lift Your name up higher.

  We will draw near,
  And surrender our fear;
  Lift our hands to proclaim
  Holy Father, You are here.

Spirit of God, come in
And release our hearts to praise You.
Make us whole, for
Holy we'll become, and serve You.

Show us Your power, we pray,
That we might share in Your glory.
We shall arise and go
To proclaim Your works most holy.

102 Graham Kendrick.

LORD HAVE MERCY on us,
Come and heal our land.
Cleanse with Your fire, heal with Your touch,
Humbly we bow and call upon You now.
O Lord, have mercy on us,
O Lord, have mercy on us.
  (Last time only)
O Lord, have mercy on us.

103 Graham Kendrick.

LORD, HAVE MERCY ON THIS NATION,
For the sake of Jesus Christ.
  (Repeat—First time only)

Cleanse us, heal us, save us,
For the sake of Jesus Christ.

104 Eddie Espinosa.

LORD, I'LL SEEK AFTER YOU,
'Cause You're the only one that satisfies,
Turn toward to kiss Your face.

  And as I draw near to You
  I will give You my love;
  I will give You my self;
  I will give You my life.

Lord, I'll seek after You,
'Cause You're the only one that satisfies,
Bow down to seek Your face.

105
Eddie Espinosa.
Copyright © Mercy Publishing/
Thankyou Music 1982.

LORD, I LOVE YOU,
You alone did hear my cry;
Only You can mend this broken heart of mine.
Yes, I love You, and there is no doubt,
Lord, You've touched me from the inside out.

106
Dave Bilbrough.
Copyright © Dave Bilbrough Songs/
Thankyou Music 1985.

LORD, IN FULL AND GLAD SURRENDER,
I open up my heart, I open up my life.
In You I've found my lasting treasure
For You are my Lord, the Pearl of greatest
  worth.
I worship You, I worship You,
I will celebrate and sing of my love for You.
I worship You, I worship You,
Because of Your love these words I'll sing:
I worship You.

107
Dave Bilbrough.
Copyright © Dave Bilbrough Songs/
Thankyou Music 1987.

LORD, I WILL CELEBRATE YOUR LOVE,
From deep within my heart,
I celebrate Your love;
I celebrate Your love given to me.

You are the one that I adore;
Lord, in Your presence is life forever more;
The one that I adore.
You are my Lord.

Healing me, releasing me,
More and more reveal Yourself in me,
My Lord, my Lord!

108
Jessy Dixon/Randy Scruggs/John W. Thompson.
Copyright © 1983 Whole Armor Publishing Co./
Full Armor Publishing Co./Dixon Music.

LORD OF LORDS, King of kings,
Maker of heaven and earth and all good things,
We give You glory.
Lord Jehovah, Son of Man,
Precious Prince of Peace and the great I AM,
We give You glory.

  Glory to God!
  Glory to God!
  Glory to God Almighty
  In the highest!

Lord, You're righteous in all Your ways.
We bless Your holy name and we will give You
  praise,
We give You glory.
You reign forever in majesty,
We praise You and lift You up for eternity,
We give You glory.

109
Ian Townend.
Copyright © Thankyou Music 1986.

LORD, RELEASE MY MOUTH
That I might sing Your praises,
Lord, release my heart
That I might worship You.
Lord, release my spirit
That I might be a channel,
For the glory of the Lord to come down!

110
Graham Kendrick.
Copyright © Make Way Music/
Thankyou Music 1987.

LORD, THE LIGHT OF YOUR LOVE is shining,
In the midst of the darkness, shining;
Jesus, Light of the world, shine upon us,
Set us free by the truth You now bring us
Shine on me, shine on me.

  Shine, Jesus, shine,
  Fill this land with the Father's glory;
  Blaze, Spirit, blaze,
  Set our hearts on fire.
  Flow, river, flow,
  Flood the nations with grace and mercy;
  Send forth Your word,
  Lord, and let there be light.

Lord, I come to Your awesome presence,
From the shadows into Your radiance;
By the blood I may enter Your brightness,
Search me, try me, consume all my darkness.
Shine on me, shine on me.

As we gaze on Your kingly brightness
So our faces display Your likeness.
Ever changing from glory to glory,
Mirrored here may our lives tell Your story.
Shine on me, shine on me.

111
Bill Dobrenen.
Copyright © Mercy Publishing/
Thankyou Music 1982.

LORD, WE ASK THAT YOU WOULD come right
  now,
Jesus, come and heal me now,
Spirit, come and fill me now,
I love You.

Lord, we ask that You would come right now,
Jesus, come and heal us now,
Spirit, come and fill us now,
We love You (we love You)
We love You (we love You)
We love You, yes we do.

112

Mick Ray.
Copyright © Thankyou Music 1987.

LORD, WE GIVE YOU PRAISE;
Our prayer of thanks to You we bring.
We sing our songs to You,
For praise belongs to You;
Lord, we give You praise.

Your love goes on and on;
You never change, You never turn.
Our hands we raise to You,
And bring our praise to You;
Lord, we give You praise.

113

Trish Morgan, Ray Goudie,
Ian Townend, Dave Bankhead.
Copyright © Thankyou Music 1986.

LORD, WE LONG FOR YOU to move in power;
There's a hunger deep within our hearts,
To see healing in our nation.
Send Your Spirit to revive us:

Heal our nation,
Heal our nation,
Heal our nation,
Pour out Your Spirit on this land.

Lord we hear Your Spirit, coming closer,
A mighty wave to break upon our land,
Bringing justice, and forgiveness.
God we cry to You, 'revive us':

114

Graham Kendrick.
Copyright © Make Way Music/
Thankyou Music 1986.

LORD, YOU ARE SO PRECIOUS TO ME,
Lord, You are so precious to me,
And I love You,
Yes, I love You,
Because You first loved me.

Lord, You are so gracious to me,
Lord, You are so gracious to me,
And I love You,
Yes, I love You,
Because You first loved me.

115

Lynn DeShazo.
Copyright © Integrity's Hosanna! Music/
Thankyou Music 1982.

LORD, YOU ARE THE HOLY ONE,
And by Your grace we come
To sing this song to You,
We delight ourselves in You.
Forever You're the same,
We magnify Your name,
And of Your deeds we tell,
Holy One of Israel.

Lord, You are holy, holy,
And You are worthy to be praised.
Father, we love You, love You;
There is no other who shall reign.

116

Don Moen.
Copyright © Integrity's Hosanna! Music 1989.

LORD, YOU'RE FAITHFUL AND JUST,
In You I put my trust, mighty God,
Everlasting Father.
Your word is faithful and true,
What You promised You will do, oh Lord.
Your word endures forever.

You're faithful, faithful, and Your mercy
*   never ends;*
The world will pass away, but Your words
*   are here to stay.*
You're wonderful, Counsellor, Mighty God.
Lord Jehovah, You are the great I AM.

117

Dave Bilbrough.
Copyright © Dave Bilbrough Songs/
Thankyou Music 1985.

LORD, YOU SET MY HEART ON FIRE,
Lord, You are my one desire,
Lord, You made my burden lighter
And all I want is to give You the glory.
Lord, You make me turn from my dreaming,
Lord, You gave my life a new meaning,
Lord, You are the one I'm believing
And all I want is to give You the glory.

You, only You
Have turned my night to day;
I'm living for You, only You,
Your love is never gonna fade away.

118

MAKE A JOYFUL MELODY,
Join together in harmony,
We are a part of a family,
The family of God.

His Spirit is our guarantee
That He lives in you and me,
We are a part of a family,
The family of God.

> *Lord, we praise You, praise You,*
> *Your love is great!*
> *Lord, we praise You, praise You,*
> *We celebrate!*

119

MAKE WAY, make way, for Christ the King
In splendour arrives.
Fling wide the gates and welcome Him
Into your lives.

> *Make way! (Make way!)*
> *Make way! (Make way!)*
> *For the King of kings*
> *(For the King of kings)*
> *Make way! (Make way!)*
> *Make way! (Make way!)*
> *And let His kingdom in.*

He comes the broken hearts to heal,
The prisoners to free.
The deaf shall hear, the lame shall dance,
The blind shall see.

And those who mourn with heavy hearts,
Who weep and sigh;
With laughter, joy and royal crown
He'll beautify.

We call you now to worship Him
As Lord of all.
To have no gods before Him,
Their thrones must fall!

120

MAY THE FRAGRANCE of Jesus fill this
place. *(Men)*
May the fragrance of Jesus fill this
place. *(Women)*
May the fragrance of Jesus fill this place. *(Men)*
Lovely fragrance of Jesus, *(Women)*
Rising from the sacrifice *(All)*
Of lives laid down in adoration.

May the glory of Jesus fill His church. *(Men)*
May the glory of Jesus fill His church. *(Women)*
May the glory of Jesus fill His church. *(Men)*
Radiant glory of Jesus, *(Women)*
Shining from our faces *(All)*
As we gaze in adoration.

May the beauty of Jesus fill my life. *(Men)*
May the beauty of Jesus fill my life. *(Women)*
May the beauty of Jesus fill my life. *(Men)*
Perfect beauty of Jesus, *(Women)*
Fill my thoughts my words my deeds *(All)*
My all I give in adoration.

121

MAY WE BE A SHINING LIGHT to the nations,
A shining light to the peoples of the earth;
Till the whole world sees the glory of Your
name,
May Your pure light shine through us.

May we bring a word of hope to the nations,
A word of life to the peoples of the earth;
Till the whole world knows there's salvation
through Your name,
May Your mercy flow through us.

May we be a healing balm to the nations,
A healing balm to the peoples of the earth;
Till the whole world knows the power of Your
name,
May Your healing flow through us.

May we sing a song of joy to the nations,
A song of praise to the peoples of the earth;
Till the whole world rings with the praises of
Your name,
May Your song be sung through us.

May Your kingdom come to the nations,
Your will be done to the peoples of the earth;
Till the whole world knows that Jesus Christ is
    Lord,
May Your kingdom come in us,
May Your kingdom come in us,
May Your kingdom come on earth.

122
Graham Kendrick.
Copyright © Make Way Music/
Thankyou Music 1986.

MEEKNESS AND MAJESTY,
Manhood and Deity,
In perfect harmony,
The Man who is God.
Lord of eternity
Dwells in humanity,
Kneels in humility
And washes our feet.

> *O what a mystery,*
> *Meekness and majesty.*
> *Bow down and worship*
> *For this is your God,*
> *This is your God.*

Father's pure radiance,
Perfect in innocence,
Yet learns obedience
To death on a cross.
Suffering to give us life,
Conquering through sacrifice,
And as they crucify
Prays: 'Father forgive.'

Wisdom unsearchable,
God the invisible,
Love indestructible
In frailty appears.
Lord of infinity,
Stooping so tenderly,
Lifts our humanity
To the heights of His throne.

123
Maggi Dawn.
Copyright © Thankyou Music 1986.

MIGHTY GOD, gracious King, strong Deliverer;
You have heard all our prayers, and You've
    answered;
So we give to You our deep appreciation,
You're the living God, You are Lord;
You're the living God, You are Lord.

124
Jude del Hierro.
Copyright © Mercy Publishing/
Thankyou Music 1987.

MORE LOVE (more love),
MORE POWER (more power),
More of You in my life.
More love (more love),
More power (more power),
More of You in my life.

> *And I will worship You with all my heart,*
> *And I will worship You with all my mind,*
> *And I will worship You with all of my*
>   *strength,*
> *For You are my Lord.*

(Last time)
And I will seek Your face with all of my heart,
And I will seek Your face with all of my mind,
And I will seek Your face with all of my strength,
For You are my Lord,
You are my Lord.

125
Wynne Goss.
Copyright © Morningsong Music Publishing 1988.

MY GOD SHALL SUPPLY all of my needs
According to His riches in glory:
My God shall supply all of my needs
According to His word.

Seek first the kingdom of God and His
    righteousness,
And all these things shall be added unto you.
(Repeat)

By faith the righteous shall gain their
    inheritance,
If they believe in the promises of God.
(Repeat)

Call on the name of the Lord God Almighty,
He is the One who will take away all fear.
(Repeat)

126
David Fellingham.
Copyright © Thankyou Music 1988.

MY SOUL LONGS FOR YOU, O my God,
I seek You with all of my heart.
In this dry and thirsty land
My voice cries out to You;
Only Your presence can satisfy my need.

And so I enter into Your sanctuary,
To behold Your glory.
I'll give You my praise as long as I live,
Raise my hands, my life I'll give
To You, oh I love You Lord.

127

OH, THE JOY OF YOUR FORGIVENESS,
Slowly sweeping over me;
Now in heartfelt adoration
This praise I'll bring
To You, my King,
I'll worship You, my Lord.

128

O LORD, HAVE MERCY ON ME, and heal me;
O Lord, have mercy on me, and free me.
Place my feet upon a rock,
Put a new song in my heart, in my heart.
O Lord, have mercy on me.

O Lord, may Your love and Your grace, protect
me;
O Lord, may Your ways and Your truth, direct
me.
Place my feet upon a rock,
Put a new song in my heart, in my heart.
O Lord, have mercy on me.

129

O LORD, OUR LORD, how excellent is Your
name in all the earth.
O Lord, our Lord, how excellent is Your
name in all the earth.

You have set Your glory above the heavens,
From children's lips You have ordained praise.
You have set the moon and the stars in place,
And You still remember me.

What is man that You are mindful of him,
The son of man that you take care of him?
You have put everything beneath his feet,
And made him ruler of Your works.

130

O LORD, THE CLOUDS ARE GATHERING,
The fire of judgement burns,
How we have fallen!
O Lord, You stand appalled
To see Your laws of love so scorned,
And lives so broken.

Have mercy, Lord (Men)
Have mercy, Lord (Women)
Forgive us, Lord (Men)
Forgive us, Lord (Women)
Restore us, Lord
Revive Your church again } (All)
Let justice flow (Men)
Let justice flow (Women)
Like rivers (Men)
Like rivers (Women)
And righteousness like a } (All)
Never failing stream.

O Lord, over the nations now
Where is the dove of peace?
Her wings are broken.
O Lord, while precious children starve
The tools of war increase;
Their bread is stolen.

O Lord, dark powers are poised to flood
Our streets with hate and fear;
We must awaken!
O Lord, let love reclaim the lives
That sin would sweep away
And let Your kingdom come.

Yet, O Lord, Your glorious cross shall tower
Triumphant in this land,
Evil confounding.
Through the fire Your suffering church display
The glories of her Christ:
Praises resounding!

131

O LORD YOUR TENDERNESS
Melting all my bitterness,
O Lord, I receive Your love.
O Lord, Your loveliness
Changing all my ugliness,
O Lord, I receive Your love,
O Lord, I receive Your love.

132

O MAGNIFY THE LORD with me,
And let us exalt His name together.
O magnify the Lord with me,
And let us exalt His name together.

I called to the Lord and He answered,
Saved me from all of my trouble;
He delivered me from all my fear,
So I'll rejoice, I'll rejoice!

We will boast about the Lord,
Tell of the things He has done;
Let the whole world hear about it,
And they'll rejoice, they'll rejoice!

We will magnify Jesus together;
We will magnify You, O Lord.
We will magnify Jesus together;
We will magnify You, O Lord.

133 Brian Smithyman.
Copyright © Coronation Music Publishing 1988.

O MY GOD YOU ARE SO GLORIOUS,
Triumphant victorious,
Reigning supreme;
Your kingdom will increase
Your power will never cease,
Till every knee, nation and power,
Will bow before You.

134 Carl Tuttle.
Copyright © Mercy Publishing/
Thankyou Music 1985.

OPEN YOUR EYES, see the glory of the King.
Lift up your voice and His praises sing.
I love You, Lord, I will proclaim:
Hallelujah, I bless Your name.

135 Phil Rogers.
Copyright © Thankyou Music 1988.

O, THAT YOU WOULD BLESS ME,
And enlarge my borders,
That Your hand would be with me,
O Lord, O Lord.
O, that You would keep me,
Keep me from all evil,
So that I may not be ashamed,
O Lord, O Lord.

May Your kingdom come,
May Your will be done
On earth as it is in heaven;
May Your kingdom come,
May Your will be done
Through me, O Lord, O Lord.

O, that You would fill me,
Fill me with Your Spirit,
So that I may know Your power,
O Lord, O Lord.
O, that You would use me
To fulfil Your purposes,
That through me Your glory would shine,
O Lord, O Lord.

136 Patricia Morgan.
Copyright © Thankyou Music 1986.

OUT OF YOUR GREAT LOVE, You have relented.
Out of Your great love, You have shown us
    grace.
Though we've caused You pain, and we have
    hurt You,
Out of Your great love, You've turned again.

137 Graham Kendrick.
Copyright © Make Way Music/
Thankyou Music 1988.

O WHAT A MYSTERY I SEE,
What marvellous design,
That God should come as one of us,
A Son in David's line.
Flesh of our flesh, of woman born,
Our humanness He owns;
And for a world of wickedness
His guiltless blood atones.

This perfect Man, incarnate God,
By selfless sacrifice
Destroyed our sinful history,
All fallen Adam's curse.
In Him the curse to blessing turns,
My barren spirit flowers,
As over the shattered power of sin
The cross of Jesus towers.

By faith a child of His I stand,
An heir in David's line,
Royal descendant by His blood
Destined by Love's design.
Fathers of faith, my fathers now!
Because in Christ I am,
And all God's promises in Him
To me are 'Yes, Amen'!

No more then as a child of earth
Must I my lifetime spend—
His history, His destiny
Are mine to apprehend.
Oh what a Saviour, what a Lord,
O Master, Brother, Friend!
What miracle has joined me to
This life that never ends!

138

PEACE TO YOU.
We bless you now in the name of the Lord.
Peace to you.
We bless you now in the name of the Prince of
   Peace.
Peace to you.

139

PRAISE HIM, praise Him,
Praise Him with your song.
Praise Him, praise Him,
Praise Him all day long!

   For the Lord is worthy,
   Worthy to receive our praise.
   For the Lord is worthy,
   Worthy to receive our praise.

Praise Him, praise Him,
Praise Him with your heart.
Praise Him, praise Him,
Give Him all you are.

Praise Him, praise Him,
Praise Him with your life.
Praise Him, praise Him,
Lift His name up high.

140

PRAISE THE LORD, praise Him in His temple,
Praise Him in the sanctuary of His power.
Lift your voices with great rejoicing,
For God is great in all the earth.

Praise Him for His excellence,
Praise Him for His love;
Praise Him for His mercy,
Giving us new life.

141

RAISE UP AN ARMY, O God,
Awake Your people throughout the earth.
Raise up an army, O God,
To proclaim Your kingdom,
To declare Your word,
To declare Your glory, O God.

Our hope, our heart, our vision,
To see in every land
Your chosen people coming forth.
Fulfilling Your holy mission,
United as we stand,
Pledging our lives unto You, Lord.

O God, our glorious Maker,
We marvel at Your grace,
That You would use us in Your plan.
Rejoicing at Your favour,
Delighting in Your ways,
We'll gladly follow Your command!

142

REIGN IN ME, sovereign Lord,
Reign in me.
Reign in me, sovereign Lord,
Reign in me.
Captivate my heart,
Let Your kingdom come,
Establish there Your throne,
Let Your will be done.

143

REKINDLE YOUR FIRST LOVE in my heart,
I never intended to depart
From the trusting child I was
Simply knowing that because
You are my Father, I am Your child,
I am acceptable.

You've never changed, and You never will,
I open my heart to embrace Your will.
I love You, I trust You, my dear Father;
Rekindle Your first love in me.

144

RISE UP, you champions of God,
Rise up, you royal nation;
Rise up, and bear His light abroad,
We'll reach this generation.
We've got our marching orders,
We've got our marching orders;
Now is the time to carry them forth.

Go forth! Jesus loves them.
Go forth! Take the gospel.
Go forth! The time is now.
The harvest is ripening;
Go forth!

Feel now the burden of the Lord,
Feel how He longs to save them;
Feel now for those who never heard
About the Son He gave them.
We've got our marching orders,
We've got our marching orders;
Now is the time to carry them forth.

145

Hilary Davies.
Copyright © Samsongs Music/
Thankyou Music 1988.

SEE HIM COME, the King upon a donkey.
Where is all His majesty and power?
He who was glorious, yet for my sake
Put away glory to die upon the cross.
His body was broken,
His heart was torn apart for me upon the cross.

See the people line His path with palm leaves;
Hear the children shouting out His name.
He who was glorious, yet for my sake
Put away power to die upon the cross.
His body was broken,
His heart was torn apart for me upon the cross.

146

Wes Sutton.
Copyright © Word (UK) 1988

SEND THE RAIN, LORD, let it come, Lord,
On this people, in this hour.
Let the rain fall on this dry ground,
Touch the earth, Lord, with Your power.
Let refreshing water flow, Lord,
Cause Your life to make us live;
Make this nation into the garden
With the fragrance of Your love.

Send the fire, Lord, from the altar;
Cleanse this nation with Your blood.
Let Your Spirit birth within us
Heartfelt turning back to God.
Let Your Spirit cleanse and heal us.
Let Your glory be displayed;
Let Your kingdom come among us,
Show the earth Your gracious reign.

147

David Fellingham.
Copyright © Thankyou Music 1988.

SHOUT FOR JOY AND SING your praises to the
  King,
Lift your voice and let your hallelujahs ring;
Come before His throne to worship and adore,
Enter joyfully now the presence of the Lord.

You are my Creator, You are my Deliverer,
You are my Redeemer, You are Lord,
And You are my Healer.
You are my Provider,
You are now my Shepherd and my Guide,
Jesus, Lord and King, I worship You.

148

Graham Kendrick.
Copyright © Make Way Music/
Thankyou Music 1988.

SHOW YOUR POWER, O LORD,
Demonstrate the justice of Your kingdom.
Prove Your mighty word.
Vindicate Your name
Before a watching world.
Awesome are Your deeds, O Lord;
Renew them for this hour.
Show Your power, O Lord,
Among the people now.

Show Your power, O Lord,
Cause Your church to rise and take action.
Let all fear be gone,
Powers of the age to come
Are breaking through.
We Your people are ready to serve,
To arise and to obey.
Show Your power, O Lord,
And set the people free.
    (Ending last time)
Show Your power, O Lord,
And set the people—
Show Your power, O Lord,
And set the people—
Show Your power, O Lord,
And set the people free.

149

Graham Kendrick.
Copyright © Make Way Music/
Thankyou Music 1988.

SOFTEN MY HEART, Lord,
Soften my heart,
From all indifference
Set me apart.
To feel Your compassion,
To weep with Your tears;
Come soften my heart, O Lord,
Soften my heart.

150 John Wimber.
Copyright © Maranatha! Music USA/
Word Music UK 1979.

SON OF GOD, this is our praise song.
Jesus, my Lord, I sing to You.
Come now, Spirit of God,
Breathe life into these words of love;
Angels join from above
As we sing our praise song.

We praise You, we praise You,
We praise You, we worship You.
We praise You, we worship You.

Son of God, this is our love song.
Jesus, my Lord, I sing to You.
Come now, Spirit of God,
Breathe life into these words of love;
Angels join from above
As we sing our love song.

We love You, we love You,
We love You, we worship You.
We love You, we worship You.

151 James Anderson.
Copyright © Soundtruth/Coronation Music/
Thankyou Music 1988.

SOUND THE CALL to worship,
Come before the King;
Bring your songs of praise to Him,
Lift your voice and sing.
Let our God be magnified,
Let our God be magnified,
And let all those who love your salvation
Say God be magnified.

152 Paul Armstrong.
Copyright © Restoration Music Ltd 1984.

SPIRIT OF THE LIVING GOD
Fall afresh on me,
Spirit of the living God
Fall afresh on me.
Fill me anew,
Fill me anew.
Spirit of the Lord
Fall afresh on me.

153 Graham Kendrick.
Copyright © Make Way Music/
Thankyou Music 1988.

SUCH LOVE, pure as the whitest snow;
Such love, weeps for the shame I know;
Such love, paying the debt I owe;
O Jesus, such love.

Such love, stilling my restlessness;
Such love, filling my emptiness;
Such love, showing me holiness;
O Jesus, such love.

Such love, springs from eternity;
Such love, streaming through history;
Such love, fountain of life to me;
O Jesus, such love.

154 Chris A. Bowater.
Copyright © Lifestyle Ministries/
Word Music (UK) 1986.

SWING WIDE THE GATES,
Let the King come in;
Swing wide the gates,
Make a way for Him.
Here He comes, the King of Glory,
Here He comes, mighty in victory,
Here He comes, in splendour and majesty.
Swing wide the gates,
Swing wide the gates,
Let the King come in.

155 John Daniels.
Copyright © Thankyou Music 1986.

TEACH ME YOUR WAY, O Lord,
And I will walk in Your truth;
Give me an undivided heart,
That I may fear Your name.

And I will praise You, O Lord my God,
With all of my heart;
And I will praise You, O Lord my God,
And I will glorify Your name forever.

156 Graham Kendrick.
Copyright © Make Way Music/
Thankyou Music 1985.

THANK YOU FOR THE CROSS,
The price You paid for us,
How You gave Yourself,
So completely,
Precious Lord, (precious Lord).
Now our sins are gone,
All forgiven,
Covered by Your blood,
All forgotten,
Thank You Lord, (thank You Lord).

Oh I love You, Lord,
Really love You, Lord.
I will never understand
Why You love me.
You're my deepest joy,
You're my heart's desire,
And the greatest thing of all, O Lord, I see:
You delight in me!

For our healing there
Lord You suffered,
And to take our fear
You poured out Your love,
Precious Lord, (precious Lord).
Calvary's work is done,
You have conquered,
Able now to save
So completely,
Thank You Lord, (thank You Lord).

157

Dave Bilbrough.
Copyright © Dave Bilbrough Songs/
Thankyou Music 1985.

THE CHURCH'S ONE FOUNDATION
Is Jesus Christ the Lord,
And on that revelation,
Each one of us is called
To taste His full salvation,
To know His life within;
A pure and holy nation
To glorify the King.

Hallelujah, how great You are,
Reigning in glory, enthroned in power;
Bright Morning Star, how great You are;
Reigning in glory, enthroned in power.

This time of preparation
Eventually will yield
The fruit of all His labours;
His heart will be fulfilled.
From every tribe and nation
His people shall be known;
Drawn to be His kingdom,
Made out of living stones.

See Him and be radiant,
Taste the Lord and know
He wants to take us deeper,
For what we are we sow;
With streams of living water
He longs to overflow,
That out to all creation
His glory He will show.

158

Jimmy Anderson.
Copyright © Soundtruth Publishing/
Thankyou Music 1988.

THE LORD GOD REIGNS, and makes His glory
known
Throughout all creation.
The Lord God reigns, and makes His glory
known
Throughout all creation.
And the whole earth sings with one voice,
Jehovah God is King of kings;
And the whole earth sings with one voice,
Lord of lords, forever let us sing,
Lord of lords, forever let us sing.

159

Graham Kendrick.
Copyright © Make Way Music/
Thankyou Music 1988.

THE LORD IS A MIGHTY KING, *(Men)*
The Maker of everything. *(Women)*
The Lord He made the earth, *(Men)*
He spoke, and it came at once to
birth. *(Women)*
He said, 'Let Us make mankind,' *(Men)*
The crown of His design, *(Women)*
'In Our own likeness,' *(Men)*
His image in every human face. *(Women)*

(All)
And He made us for His delight,
Gave us the gift of life,
Created us family,
To be His glory,
To be His glory.

And yet we were deceived *(Men)*
In pride the lie believed *(Women)*
To sin and death's decay— *(Men)*
The whole creation fell that day. *(Women)*
Now all creation *(Men)*
Yearns for liberation; *(Women)*
All things in Christ restored— *(Men)*
The purchase of His precious blood. *(Women)*

160

Graham Kendrick.
Copyright © Make Way Music/
Thankyou Music 1986.

THE LORD IS MARCHING OUT in splendour,
In awesome majesty He rides,
For truth, humility and justice,
His mighty army fills the skies.

O give thanks to the Lord for His love
endures,
O give thanks to the Lord for His love
endures,
O give thanks to the Lord for His love
endures,
For ever, for ever.

His army marches out with dancing
For He has filled our hearts with joy.
Be glad the kingdom is advancing,
The love of God our battle cry!

161 Author unknown.

THE LORD YOUR GOD IS IN YOUR MIDST
The Lord of lords His name;
He will exult over you with joy,
He will renew you in His love,
He will rejoice over you
With shouts of joy, shouts of joy.
Shouts of joy, shouts of joy,
Shouts of joy.

162 Mark Altrogge.
Copyright © People of Destiny/
Thankyou Music 1986.

THE NATIONS ARE WAITING for us,
They're dying to hear the song we sing.
The nations are waiting for us,
Waiting for the gospel we will bring,
That in each nation men might come to know
the King.

Jesus, you lead us,
Calling us onward,
A glorious army
With banners unfurled.
It's our decision
To follow Your vision,
We're on a mission,
A mission to the world.
And the nations are waiting,
The nations are waiting,
Waiting.

163 Dave Bilbrough.
Copyright © Dave Bilbrough Songs/
Thankyou Music 1985.

THERE'S A NEW WAVE COMING,
There's a new day that's dawning,
There's a fresh wind that's blowing
For the people of the Lord;
Who are sensing the freedom
Of the life He has given,
It's a time of liberation
For the people of the Lord.

God of grace, we worship You
For You alone are worthy.
God of grace, we worship You
We'll give You all the glory.

No guilt or accusation
Shall be our motivation,
But a growing revelation
Of the glory of the Lord.
We are a new creation
And by our demonstration
We reveal the incarnation
Of the glory of the Lord.

164 Chris A. Bowater.
Copyright © Lifestyle Ministries/
Word Music (UK) 1985.

THE SPIRIT OF THE LORD,
The sovereign Lord, is on me,
Because he has anointed me
To preach good news to the poor:

Proclaiming Jesus, only Jesus—
It is Jesus, Saviour, healer and baptizer,
And the mighty King,
The victor and deliverer—
He is Lord, He is Lord, He is Lord!

And he has called on me
To bind up all the broken hearts,
To minister release
To every captivated soul:

Let righteousness arise
And blossom as a garden;
Let praise begin to spring
In every tongue and nation:

165 Suella Behrns.
Copyright © Christian Fellowship of Columbia
1981.

THINE, O LORD IS THE GREATNESS,
And the power and the glory.
Thine, O Lord, is the victory,
And majesty, and majesty.

All that is in heaven and earth is Thine,
Thou art exalted as head over all!

In Thy hand is power and might to make great,
In Thy hand is power to give strength to all!

Now is come salvation and power and might
For the kingdom of our God has been given to
His Christ!

166
Debbye Graafsma.
Copyright © Integrity's Hosanna! Music 1985.

TO HIM WHO SITS ON THE THRONE and unto
the Lamb,
To Him who sits on the throne and unto the
Lamb
Be blessing and glory and honour and power for
ever,
Be blessing and glory and honour and power for
ever.

167
Phil Townend.
Copyright © Thankyou Music 1986.

UNTO YOU, O LORD
Do I open up my heart.
Unto You, O Lord
Do I lift my voice.
Unto You, O Lord
Do I raise my hands,
Unto You, O Lord of hosts.

168
Mick Gisbey.
Copyright © Thankyou Music 1988.

WE ARE ALL ASSEMBLED
Before the King of kings,
As He reveals the battle we must face.
Active in the conflict
That He has overcome,
Together being taught
How to fight:

And live in victory, victory,
Marching on the conquering side;
Victory, victory,
Jesus is our battle cry.

We are armed for battle,
Ready and alert,
Fighting in the army of our God;
Mastering the weapons
Forged by the King,
Trained to follow orders
We unite:

And soon the Prince of Peace will come,
And every eye will see
The great and shining glory of our God;
With songs of joyful triumph
Welcoming the King,
Forever giving glory
Unto Him:

169
Trevor King.
Copyright © Trevor King/
Thankyou Music 1986.

WE ARE A PEOPLE OF POWER,
We are a people of praise;
We are a people of promise,
Jesus has risen, He's conquered the grave!
Risen, yes, born again,
We walk in the power of His name;
Power to be the sons of God,
The sons of God! The sons of God!
We are the sons, sons of God!

170
Ian Smale.
Copyright © Thankyou Music 1987.

WE ARE IN GOD'S ARMY,
We are in the army of the Lord, yeah, yeah,
yeah.
We are in God's army,
We're in the Glorie, Glorie, Glorie,
the Glorie Company.

The enemy's attacking, convinced he's gaining
ground,
But the only voice that he can hear is the one he
shouts around;
But we're not fooled by his lies, we know that he
is wrong—
We may be weak as soldiers, but as an army we
are strong.

The enemy's regrouping, as he tries another
plan,
He can't pick off an army but he can pick out a
man;
So we'll stay close together, and sing this
battle-song—
We may be weak as soldiers, but as an army we
are strong.

The enemy's realising that his future's looking
poor,
Though he loves single combat, he's already
lost the war;
United, not divided, together we belong—
We may be weak as soldiers, but as an army we
are strong.

171 Martin F. Ball/Ian C. Thompson.
Copyright © Restoration Music 1987.

WE ARE STILLED by Your presence,
Captivated by Your beauty,
For Your loveliness and holiness
Amazes us, O Lord.

In abandonment of worship
We bow down in adoration,
And ascribe to You,
Yes, we ascribe to You,
The glory due to Your name.

Holy, You are holy,
Holy is the Lord.
Holy, You are holy,
Holy is the Lord.

172 David Fellingham.
Copyright © Thankyou Music 1986.

WE ARE YOUR PEOPLE who are called by Your
name.
We call upon You now to declare Your fame.
In this nation of darkness You've called us to be
light.
As we seek Your face, Lord, stir up Your might.
Build Your church and heal this land,
Let Your kingdom come.
Build Your church and heal this land,
Let Your will be done.

173 Graham Kendrick.
Copyright © Make Way Music/
Thankyou Music 1986.

WE BELIEVE in God the Father,
Maker of the universe,
And in Christ His Son our Saviour,
Come to us by virgin birth.
We believe He died to save us,
Bore our sins, was crucified.
Then from death He rose victorious,
Ascended to the Father's side.

Jesus, Lord of all, Lord of all,
Jesus, Lord of all, Lord of all,
Jesus, Lord of all, Lord of all,
Jesus, Lord of all, Lord of all.
Name above all names,
Name above all names.
Name above all names. (Last time only)

We believe He sends His Spirit,
On His church with gifts of power.
God His word of truth affirming,
Sends us to the nations now.
He will come again in glory,
Judge the living and the dead.
Every knee shall bow before Him,
Then must every tongue confess.

174 Chris Rolinson.
Copyright © Thankyou Music 1987.

WE BREAK THIS BREAD to share in the body of
Christ: *(Men)*
We break this bread to share in the body of
Christ. *(Women)*

Though we are many, we are one body,
Because we all share we all share in one
bread.
(Repeat)

We drink this cup to share in the body of
Christ: *(Men)*
We drink this cup to share in the body of
Christ. *(Women)*

175 Graham Kendrick.
Copyright © Make Way Music/
Thankyou Music 1986.

(Men and women in canon)
WE DECLARE THAT THE KINGDOM OF GOD
IS HERE,
We declare that the kingdom of God is here,
Among you, among you.

(Last time)
We declare that the kingdom of God is
here (Men)
We declare that the kingdom of God is
here (Women)
We declare that the (Men)
Kingdom of God is here. (All)

The blind see, the deaf hear,
The lame men are walking;
Sicknesses flee at His voice.
The dead live again,
And the poor hear the good news:
Jesus is King, so rejoice!

176

WE DECLARE THERE'S ONLY ONE LORD,
And the earth belongs to Him,
We proclaim the day of salvation,
It's His kingdom and He's the King.

There is none like our mighty King,
He gave His life to free us.
There is none more worthy of
Our lives and our allegiance.

177

WE HONOUR YOUR PRESENCE, Lord,
We sing with chords of grace.
The nature of Your love is mercy,
Mercy to the human race.
We humble ourselves,
Oh, we humble ourselves,
As we bow before You
To seek Your face.
We humble ourselves,
Oh, we humble ourselves,
As we bow before You
To receive the Spirit of grace.

178

WE SHALL STAND
With our feet on the Rock.
Whatever men may say,
We'll lift Your name up high.
And we shall walk
Through the darkest night.
Setting our faces like flint,
We'll walk into the light.

Lord, You have chosen me
For fruitfulness,
To be transformed into
Your likeness.
I'm gonna fight on through
'Till I see You, face to face.

Lord, as Your witnesses
You've appointed us.
And with Your Holy Spirit
Anointed us.
And so I'll fight on through,
'Till I see You, face to face.

179

**WE'VE BEEN CALLED TO CHANGE THE
  WORLD,**
Jesus we have heard Your great command.
Motivated by Your love,
We will change the world.

And we will sound the battle cry,
Let God arise!
In majesty and power,
Let God, let God arise!
We have heard the great commission.
  (World changers)
We'll go forward in the vision.
  (We're going to be world changers)
Filled with the Spirit.
Proclaiming Your word.
Jesus died for every nation.
  (World changers)
Shout it loud with jubilation.
  (We're going to be world changers.)
We're changing lives
With the love of Jesus,
And the earth shall see
The salvation of our God.

We've been called to bring new life,
Setting captives free from sin's domain,
Healing those oppressed by fear,
We will bring new life.

We've been called to fight a war,
Satan will oppose and man will rage.
Loving not our lives unto death,
We will not turn back.

We've been called to build the church,
A house of prayer for every land.
Every tribe and tongue shall sing
Glory to the Lamb!

180

WHAT CAN STAND AGAINST THE LORD,
And against the praises of His saints?
What can stand against the Lord,
And against the praises of His saints?
Lift your banners high, God our Righteousness
Is coming to His temple.
Lift your banners high, God our Righteousness
Is coming to His temple.

181

WHO CAN EVER SAY they understand
All the wonders of His master plan?
Christ came down and gave Himself to man
Forever more.

He was Lord before all time began,
Yet made Himself the sacrificial lamb,
Perfect love now reconciled to man
Forever more.

Forever more we'll sing the story
Of love come down
Forever more the King of glory
We will crown.

He is coming back to earth again,
Every knee shall bow before His name,
'Christ is Lord', let thankful hearts proclaim
Forever more.

182

WHO CAN SOUND THE DEPTHS OF SORROW
In the Father heart of God,
For the children we've rejected,
For the lives so deeply scarred?
And each light that we've extinguished
Has brought darkness to our land,
Upon our nation, upon our nation,
Have mercy Lord.

We have scorned the truth You gave us,
We have bowed to other lords.
We have sacrificed the children
On the altars of our gods.
O let truth again shine on us,
Let Your holy fear descend.
Upon our nation, upon our nation,
Have mercy, Lord.

(Men only)
Who can stand before Your anger?
Who can face Your piercing eyes?
For You love the weak and helpless,
And You hear the victims' cries.
(All)
Yes, You are a God of justice,
And Your judgement surely comes.
Upon our nation, upon our nation,
Have mercy, Lord.

(Women only)
Who will stand against the violence?
Who will comfort those who mourn?
In an age of cruel rejection,
Who will build for love a home?
(All)
Come and shake us into action,
Come and melt our hearts of stone.
Upon Your people, upon Your people,
Have mercy, Lord.

Who can sound the depths of mercy
In the Father heart of God?
For there is a Man of sorrows
Who for sinners shed His blood.
He can heal the wounds of nations,
He can wash the guilty clean.
Because of Jesus, because of Jesus,
Have mercy, Lord.

183

WITH ALL MY HEART I thank You Lord.
With all my heart I thank You Lord,
For this bread and wine we break,
For this sacrament we take,
For the forgiveness that You make,
I thank You Lord.

With all my soul I thank You Lord.
With all my soul I thank You Lord,
For this victory that You've won,
For this taste of things to come,
For this love that makes us one,
I thank You Lord.

With all my voice I thank You Lord.
With all my voice I thank You Lord,
For the sacrifice of pain,
For the Spirit and the flame,
For the power of Your name,
I thank You Lord.

184

WORSHIP THE LORD! In His presence we stand;
He cares for you and He understands.
Come Holy Spirit, reaching us now;
Grace, joy and peace, love abound.

Holy, holy, holy is the Lord.

(Additional choruses)
Worthy...
Mighty...

185 Ian White, adapt NIV.
Copyright © 1973, 1978, 1984,
International Bible Society.

WORTHY, THE LORD IS WORTHY,
And no one understands the greatness of His
name.
Gracious, so kind and gracious,
And slow to anger, and rich, so rich in love.

My mouth will speak in praise of my Lord,
Let every creature praise His holy name.
For ever, and ever more.
For ever, and ever more.
For ever, and ever more.
For ever, and ever more.

Faithful, the Lord is faithful
To all His promises, and loves all He has made.
Righteous, in all ways righteous,
And He is near to all who call on Him in truth.

186 Lynn DeShazo.
Copyright © Integrity's Hosanna! Music/
Thankyou Music 1985.

YAHWEH IS HOLY, Yahweh is holy;
Yahweh is holy, Yahweh is holy.
Yahweh is holy, Yahweh is holy;
Yahweh is holy, Yahweh is holy.

Thou art enthroned on the praises of Israel.
Thou art enthroned on the praises of Israel.
And I will trust in Thee, and stand in awe of
Thee.
I will bow and worship Yahweh,
Holy.

187 Mark Altrogge.
Copyright © People of Destiny/
Thankyou Music 1986.

YOU ARE BEAUTIFUL beyond description,
Too marvellous for words,
Too wonderful for comprehension
Like nothing ever seen or heard.
Who can grasp Your infinite wisdom?
Who can fathom the depth of Your love?
You are beautiful beyond description,
Majesty, enthroned above.

And I stand, I stand in awe of You.
I stand, I stand in awe of You.
Holy God, to whom all praise is due,
I stand in awe of You.

188 John Sellers.
Copyright © Integrity's Hosanna! Music 1984.

YOU ARE CROWNED WITH MANY CROWNS,
And rule all things in righteousness,
You are crowned with many crowns,
Upholding all things by Your word.
You rule in power and reign in glory!
You are Lord of heaven and earth!
You are Lord of all,
You are Lord of all.

189 Patty Kennedy.
Copyright © Mercy Publishing/
Thankyou Music 1985.

YOU ARE HERE and I behold Your beauty,
Your glory fills this place.
Calm my heart to hear You,
Cause my eyes to see You.
Your presence here is the answer
To the longing of my heart.

I lift my voice to worship and exalt You,
For You alone are worthy.
A captive now set free
Your kingdom's come to me.
Glory in the highest,
My heart cries unto You.

190 Bob Fraser.
Copyright © Ears and Eyes Music 1986.

YOU ARE THE ROCK on which I stand,
A strong foundation, not shifting sand;
Strengthened by Your mighty hand,
You are the rock on which I stand.

In Your mercy, Lord, You rescued me
From the darkness of my own ways;
You placed my feet upon the solid ground;
I lift my voice to sing Your praise!

Whenever life begins to wear me down,
When I need a place to hide;
You lift my Spirit with Your tender touch,
Then I know, You will provide!

191
Dave Bilbrough.
Copyright © Dave Bilbrough Songs/
Thankyou Music 1985.

**YOU BROUGHT ME BACK TO THE PLACE I
BELONG,**
You filled my life with a brand new song.
You made me see that I just can't go wrong
Now that my old life is gone.
You showed to me that the work has been done,
There's nothing I need to become.
It's unbelievable, O what a miracle,
I and the Father are one!

192
Mark Altrogge.
Copyright © People of Destiny/
Thankyou Music 1989.

YOU CAME TO SEEK and to save the captives of
sin,
When we had wandered away You gathered us
in.
You are preparing a feast, You want Your house
filled;
As you sought us, so shall we seek others, too.
This is Your will.

For You are the Lord of the harvest;
You give the increase, You're building Your
church.
You are the Lord of the harvest,
Pouring out Your Spirit in the earth,
Pouring out Your Spirit in the earth.

193
Mark Altrogge.
Copyright © People of Destiny/
Thankyou Music 1985.

YOU DID NOT WAIT FOR ME to draw near to
You,
But You clothed Yourself in frail humanity.
You did not wait for me to cry out to You,
But You let me hear Your voice calling me.

And I'm for ever grateful to You,
I'm for ever grateful for the cross;
I'm for ever grateful to You
That You came to seek and save the lost.

194
Bob Kauflin.
Copyright © People of Destiny/
Thankyou Music 1987.

YOU HAVE BEEN GIVEN the Name above all
names,
And we worship You, yes we worship You.
You have been given the Name above all
names,
And we worship You,
Yes we worship You.

We are Your people, made for Your glory,
And we worship You, yes we worship You.
We are Your people, made for Your glory,
And we worship You,
And we worship You.

You have redeemed us from every nation,
And we worship You, yes we worship You.
You have redeemed us from every nation,
And we worship You,
And we worship You.

195
Dave Markee.
Copyright © Dave Markee/
Thankyou Music 1988.

YOU NEVER CHANGE, always the same;
There is no shadow in Your brightness,
The everlasting flame of timeless love
Keeps shining on, from age to age You are the
same,
You never change.

You never change, always the same;
Your majesty rules over all,
While nations rage and kingdoms fall.
Nothing escapes Your restless gaze,
From age to age You are the Father,
Caring for Your children
With such tenderness, and endless grace;
Your faithfulness is never ending,
Yesterday, today, forever Lord.
Eternal King, I worship You,
And I'm secure because I know
You never change.

196
Mark Veary & Paul Oakley.
Copyright © Thankyou Music 1986.

YOU, O LORD, rich in mercy,
Because of Your great love.
You, O Lord, so loved us,
Even when we were dead in our sins.

(Men)
You made us alive together with Christ,
And raised us up together with Him,
And seated us with Him in heavenly places,
And raised us up together with Him,
And seated us with Him in heavenly places
in Christ.

(Women)
You made us alive together with Christ,
And raised us up,
And seated us,
And raised us up,
And seated us in Christ.

197

YOU, O LORD, ARE HOLY;
You, O Lord, are holy;
You're enthroned on the praise of Your people;
Holy is Your name.
Holy is Your name!

And I praise You, Lord;
And I bless You, Lord;
And I lift my hands
To magnify Your name.

You, O Lord, are worthy;
You, O Lord, are worthy;
I lift my hands to show You are worthy,
Worthy is Your name.
Worthy is Your name!

You, O Lord, are seated;
You, O Lord, are seated;
Seated high in heavenly places,
I set my mind on You,
I set my mind on You.

I surrender all;
I give my life to You;
Come Holy Spirit, come now,
Fill my life anew,
Fill my life anew!

198

YOU PURCHASED MEN with precious blood,
From every nation, tribe and tongue;
Brought from slavery, freed from prison chains;
Brought through death so they might rise again,
Born to serve and to reign:

Worthy is the Lamb that was slain, to receive
Highest honour, and glory, and power, and
*   praise!*
Worthy is the Lamb that was slain, to receive
Highest honour, and glory, and praise!

Holy, holy to our God,
Who was, and is, and is to come;
Let us join the throng who see His face,
Bowing down to Him both night and day,
Lost in wonder and praise.

199

YOUR MERCY FLOWS upon us like a river.
Your mercy stands unshakeable and true.
Most holy God, of all good things the Giver,
We turn and lift our fervent prayer to You.

Hear our cry,   (echo)
O Lord,   (echo)
Be merciful   (echo)
Once more;   (echo)
Let Your love   (echo)
Your anger stem,   (echo)
Remember mercy, O Lord, again.

Your church once great, though standing
    clothed in sorrow,
Is even still the bride that You adore;
Revive Your church, that we again may honour
Our God and King, our Master and our Lord.

As we have slept, this nation has been taken
By every sin ever known to man;
So at its gates, though burnt by fire and broken,
In Jesus' name we come to take our stand.

200

YOU SAT DOWN at the right hand of the Father
    in majesty,
You sat down at the right hand of the Father in
    majesty.
You are crowned Lord of all,
You are faithful and righteous and true,
You're my Master, You're my Owner,
And I love serving You.

Index of titles and first lines

(Titles where different from first lines are shown in *italics*)

Thematic index

(Arranged under the four main headings of *God the Father, Jesus, The Holy Spirit,* and *The Church*—the last section suggesting uses for songs within meetings.)

GOD THE FATHER

JESUS

THE HOLY SPIRIT

THE CHURCH

Scripture index